CHERRIE[S]
THE RISE

Their cultivation in Kent through the centuries

**If they *blow in April
You'll have your fill
But if in May,
They'll all go away.**

* blossom

Alan Major

S.B. Publications

By the same author
Hidden Kent, Countryside Books
A New Dictionary of Kent Dialect, Meresborough Books.
Who's Buried Where in Kent Meresborough Books

Dedicated to my brother
Andre Major
and our
late father, Percy Major,
also to all cherrymen and cherrywomen
who, in the past, whether involved in
the cultivation or picking, were part
of Kent's cherry history.

First published in 1997 by S. B. Publications,
c/o 19 Grove Road, Seaford, East Sussex BN25 1TP

ISBN 1 85770 117 8

Designed and typeset by CGB, Lewes
Printed by MFP Design and Print
Longford Trading Estate, Thomas Street,
Stretford, Manchester M32 0JT

CONTENTS

INTRODUCTION

IN Kent there has been the parallel cultivation of hops and cherries. The history and the up-to-date story of hops and hop growing in the county has been chronicled in numerous books but the past and present story of cherries and cherry cultivation in Kent is sparsely recorded.

It has been my intention to remedy such an omission in this book, and I hope readers will find much to interest them within its pages.

Alan Major

KENTISH CHERRIES – A ballad

The maids of Kent, as I well know
Of all fair maids are fairest,
For on their pretty lips do grow
Ripe cherries of the rarest.
Red is the first uprising streak
Which opening day discloses;
Red is the blushing lover's cheek,
And red the blush of roses;
Red is the Christmas flame which glows
On glistening holly berries;
But of a richer red than those
Are lips of Kentish cherries.

Here's to the cherry lips of Kent,
Come fill your glasses higher
And toast them till the voice is spent,
With triple Kentish fire.*
Sweet fruits grow 'neath another clime,
The orange, fig and melon,
The date, pomegranate, grape and lime
Are things one might well live on
But all these sweets of Nature's make
Or richest wines and sherries,
I'd gladly leave, one taste to take
Of those sweet Kentish cherries.'

From the Kentish Magazine, 1850.

*A form of hand clapping.

1

THE WILD CHERRIES IN KENT

THERE are two species of wild cherry in the Kent countryside: the Gean (*Prunus avium*) and Dwarf or Wild Cherry (*Prunus cerasus*).

The Gean occurs in woods and hedges, especially beech woods, reaching up to eighty feet in height (25m) in favourable conditions. The trunk has a thin, smooth, greyish or reddish-brown bark that peels off in horizontal strips with age. The long, spreading, upward direction branches have two types of shoot – elongated or very short, the short shoots producing the flowers.

In April and May the scented flowers are borne in umbels or clusters, up to six flowers in the clusters, each flower having a stalk up to one and a half inches long, and five white, notched, heart-shaped, fragile, finely veined petals.They are produced at the same time as the sharp-toothed, equally serrated, pointed, broadly-oval leaves, which are hairy on their underside and almost hidden if the flowers are profuse.The leaves only attain full size and droop from the branches when the fruit is ripe.

In spring they are deep red or bronzy brown, afterwards pale bright green and in autumn a fiery red. The fruit is small, firmly fleshed, round to heart-shaped, usually black but sometimes red, with juice that stains the fingers.

This cherry was also known locally in some areas as Clusters, referring to the blossom in umbels, and that the resulting black cherries hung in clusters.

The *avium* part of the Latin name derives from the Latin *avis* – the birds that are attracted to the ripe fruit and, by greedily swallowing and excreting the interior stone, assists in the distribution of the tree.

The first record of the Gean growing in Kent is in 1666. It is noted by Christopher Merrett in *Pinax,* his compilation of plant records published in that year, as '*Cerasus nigra,* found in several places in Kent.'

In Kent rural speech another name for this cherry is Gaskin, which may be a corruption of Gascoine, which the Reverend Dr. Samuel Pegge, vicar of Godmersham in 1735/6 described as 'small black cherries' in his

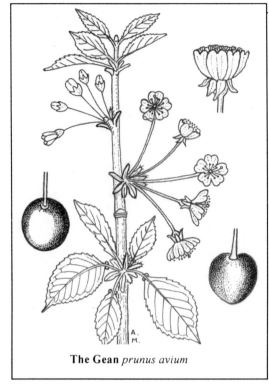

The Gean *prunus avium*

Alphabet of Kenticisms.

Black Gean cherries were gathered in the wild and sent, with cultivated black cherries, to cherry brandy makers to add flavour to the liqueur.

The Gean was also harvested by country folk to make their own cherry wine. In their *Flora of Kent* Hanbury and Marshall record it as: 'Native. Woods. Common, generally distributed. Tree. May. When in flower this adds great charm to Kentish woods.'

The Dwarf or Wild Cherry, formerly known as the Wild Red or Red-fruited Cherry, also occurs in woods, but more so in hedges or waysides as it is a small tree, only reaching a height of about 20ft (6m) at maturity. It occurs frequently as a much-branched bushy shrub due to its habit of developing a large number of suckers around its main stem.

The slender drooping branches bear pointed leaves similar to the Gean, but smaller, deep green, round-toothed, inequally and irregularly serrated, shorter stalked, smooth, also almost hairless on the under surface. In April and May the white flowers, also in umbels or clusters, do not open so wide but are more cup-shaped, the hardly-notched, thick petals being almost oval in shape. The acid, juicily fleshed fruit is round, always red, sometimes a dark red. The juice does not stain the fingers.

It was first recorded in Kent in 1777 as '*Cerasus sylvestris fructu rubro*. In woods. Common,' by Edward Jacob, a Faversham doctor who was the first Kentish palaeo-botanist and listed fossil plants found on Sheppey in his *Plantae Favershamienses*, a catalogue of plants growing about Faversham. He describes it as a shrub and the fruit red. In Kent rural speech the name for it was Mazzard. Of it Hanbury and Marshall state: 'Native, Woods and hedges; frequent but appears much rarer than *P. avium.* Shrub or small tree. May. In Kent this seems as truly wild as *P. avium*'.

It may seem these two wild cherry trees were recorded at late dates, although they were almost certainly growing in Kent centuries earlier.

What has brought this about is that the botanic history of Kent did not begin in earnest until 1548. It was then that William Turner published his *Names of Herbes,* followed by the first part of his important *Herball* in 1551.

The recording of the county's flora gradually increased, especially in the seventeenth and eighteenth centuries.

The Wild or Dwarf cherry *Prunus Cerasus*

Early history

As the Gean and Dwarf or Wild Cherry are native to Kent as wild trees they would have been found growing there by the Romans when they invaded Britain.

The Roman general, Lucullus, had won a major victory in Pontus, a Black Sea state, and according to Pliny the Elder: 'Before the victory of Lucullus, that is down to 74 BC, there were no cherry trees in Italy. Lucullus first imported them from Pontus (in 70 BC) and in 120 years they have crossed the ocean and got as far as Britain'.

As wild cherries were widespread throughout Europe it is assumed Pliny was referring to cultivated varieties of the wild cherries. He also obligingly described the cherry varieties being cultivated in Italy at this time. Of them he wrote: 'The Apronian are the reddest and the Lutatian the blackest, while the Caecilian kind are perfectly round. The Junian cherry has an agreeable flavour but practically only if eaten under the tree on which it grows, as it is so delicate it does not stand carriage. The highest rank, however, belongs to the Bigaroon (Duracina, the hard berry) cherry, called by the Campanians the Plinian cherry.'

It is not possible, with certainty, to identify the varieties Pliny was referring to, but John Gibson author of *The Fruit Gardener,* 1768, suggested the Apronian was what came to be known as the Cluster cherry; the Lutatian the Mazzard (*P. cerasus*); the Caecilian the Kentish Red; the Junian was the French Guigne; the Bigaroon or Duracina the Bigarreau Heart cherry. Bigarreau, meaning a cherry with firm flesh, was added by breeders and growers to the variety name to describe this flesh quality, thus Napoleon Bigarreau, Gaucher Bigarreau, although when marketing the group name was sometimes omitted.

If Pliny's account is correct regarding cherries in Britain it means they arrived here, namely in Kent, via the Romans about 46 AD, shortly after the invasion by Aurelius Plautus. However Pliny contradicts himself in his *Natural History,* Vol XV, in which he dates the introduction of cherries to this country as 'after 50 AD'.

Lucullus, after his campaign in Pontus and Asia Minor, may also have introduced cherries into Italy from Cerasus (now Keresoun, Asia Minor) where cherries were being grown at this time, and from which the *cerasus* part of the Dwarf or Wild Cherry's Latin name is derived.

Kent was the first region of Britain to be invaded and cultivated by the Roman colonists and it is possible that they took advantage of its favourable climate and soil to import and plant young, cultivated cherry trees.

The Royal Horticultural Society's *Dictionary of Gardening* refers to the Romans first planting cherries in Britain about 100 AD, having themselves obtained varieties from Asia Minor about 70 BC. I am inclined to agree that 100 AD is a more feasible approximate date by which the Romans could have established cherry cultivation producing a crop in

Kent. Possibly the two wild cherry species of today were growing in Kent before the Roman invasion and the Romans, noting them flourishing either:

a) introduced their own improved varieties to grow in settlement orchards, or

b) they took the better wild cherry examples they found and developed improved varieties from them. After the Romans left both these policies were perhaps followed by the early Kent cherry growers.

Early sales

An indication of just how early in Kent history cherries were being grown commercially is given by John Lydgate (1370–1451), a man of several talents. In his poem *London Lickpenny* he tells of a poor man of Kent who goes to seek his fortune in the big city and sees cherries on sale in the streets. But having no money he could not buy and finding London inhospitable, returned to Kent:

> Then unto London I dyd me hye
> Of all the land it beareth the pryse
> 'Hot pescodes' one began to cry
> 'Strabery rype' and 'cherryes in the rise!'
> And bade me come near to buy. . .

The expression 'cherries in the rise' – the cry of the street sellers, and also the title of this book – is used because a 'rise' in Kent dialect is a twig. It was customary for the sellers to tie some cherries to a rise or twig, preferably a cherry twig if one could be obtained, and carry it to advertise their wares. Potential customers were allowed to pluck one from the rise as a free sample before deciding whether to buy.

Cherries for the church

In the fourteenth century cherries were also being grown 'in the service of the church'. There is a reference in the Reeve's Account of the Manor of Teynham, *c* 1376, to twenty pence as payment for *ciresis* (cherries) 'beside cherries sent to the lord'.

The 'lord', in this instance, would have been the Archbishop of Canterbury. The Manor of Teynham had an archiespiscopal palace and was therefore church land, belonging to the Archbishop and Christ

Church, Canterbury. It was demesne land – that held in the owner's hands for his own use – and thus not let to tenants.

The payment referred to in the reeve's account is in a list of stock and sales of grain, livestock, timber and other items. It does not make clear if the Manor of Teynham sold some cherries for twenty pence or whether that was the sum paid by the reeve or steward for the purchase of cherries, perhaps for the consumption by the Archbishop when visiting his palace.

This entry in the accounts raises several questions. Did the monks of Christ Church, Canterbury, cultivate cherries themselves on their own land, or perhaps employ others to do so and sell part of the crop? Were there cherry trees in private cultivation outside the boundaries of the manor from which the reeve made his purchase? Or did the Archbishop, through his steward, rent some land to independent growers and buy some of their produce?

Whatever is correct there is a clear indication from the entry that cherries were being cultivated in the Teynham area some 200 years before the ones grown in Kent by Henry VIII's gardener, Richard Harris.

In was normal practice in the late Middle Ages for gifts of food to be sent to the Archbishop of Canterbury. The Reverend Canon Derek Ingram Hill, Canon Emeritus of Canterbury, told me of the occasion when Archbishop Cranmer was enthroned at Canterbury in December 1533. The Prior and convent of Christ Church did as they were required to and supplied a large number of swans and partridges from their lands for the banquet. Three weeks later they had nothing much left for a Christmas gift so they sent a dish of apples to the palace. No doubt some cherries from a local orchard would have been equally appreciated.

2

THE SIXTEENTH CENTURY – AND AFTER

THERE is little known about the amount of cherry cultivation in Kent between the fourteenth and sixteenth centuries. It probably continued as before in small acreages to supply ecclesiastical and commercial outlets.

Thomas Fuller, in his *Worthies of Kent*, credits Flemish refugees with introducing cherries into the county in the mid sixteenth century and John Aubrey, in his *Brief Lives*, says: 'Cherries were first brought into Kent in the reign of Henry VIII, the king, being in Flanders and liking the cherries, ordered his gardener, Richard Harris, who brought them hence and propagated them in England.

In 1576 William Lambarde, in his *A Perambulation of Kent* wrote: 'Here we have not only the most dainty pieces of all our shire but such a singularity as the whole British island is not able to pattern. . . This Tenham, with 30 other parishes extending from Rainham to Blean Wood, be the Cherry Garden and Apple Orchard of Kent. But as this at Tenham is the parent of all the rest and from whom they have drawn the good juice of all their pleasant fruit, so is it also the most large, delightsome and beautiful of them. . . Here our honest Patriot, Richard Harrys, fruiterer to King Henry VIII, planted by his great cost and rare industrie the sweet cherry, the temperate pippin and the golden renate'. (The latter is a late dessert apple – now Golden Reinette, similar to Blenheim Orange).

'He, about the year of Our Lord Christ, 1533, obtained 105 acres of good ground in the parish of Tenham, then called The Brennet, which he divided up into ten parcels and with great care, good choice and no small labour and cost, brought plants from beyond the seas and furnished this ground with them so beautifully, as they not only stand in most right line, but seem to be of one sort, shape and fashion, as if they had been drawn through one mould, or wrought by one and the same pattern'.

He goes on to say that 'the plants our ancestors had brought out of Normandy had lost their native verdour', indicating that Harris's cultivation of cherries was not the first in the county and that new stock had to be imported due to the decline of earlier locally grown imported stock.

Osier Farm, Teynham, site of the first commercial cherry planting in Kent, pictured in the 1980s when the cherry trees were still being cultivated.

A cherry orchard in full bloom, like this one at Doddington, south of Sittingbourne, was formerly a common sight in Kent

According to the NF who wrote *The Fruiterer's Secrets* in 1684, the Teynham orchard: 'hath been the chief mother of all other orchards for these kindes of fruits. And afore that these graftes were fetched out of France and the Low Countries'. Further praise for Harris came from another antiquarian and historian, William Camden, in his 1585 *Britannia – Kent:*

'Then saw I Tenham, not commended for health, but the parent as it were of all the choice fruit gardens and orchards of Kent and the most large and delightsome of them all, planted in the time of King Henrie the Eighth by Richard Harris his fruiterer to the public good. For thirty parishes thereabout are replenished with cherie gardens and orchards beautifully disposed in direct lines.

He goes on: Almost the whole county. . . is wonderfully fruitful in apples, also cherries. They thrive here exceedingly and cover large tracts of ground and the trees being planted in the quincunx, exhibit an agreeable view'.

The quincunx formation is the spatial arrangement of five as on a dice and was the formation of fruit tree planting by Roman fruit growers in Italy and at the period of the invasion of Kent by the Romans.

Possibly, after cultivation of cherries in Teynham had started in medieval times in a small way, the Flemings and 'the plaine industrie' of Harris had improved cherry cultivation there by replacing earlier varieties with larger fruited, more prolific, imported varieties, also increasing quantity through a better method of cultivation in the orchards.

The Harris family previously, and at the time of the cherry planting at Teynham, were associated with the Cinque Ports of Faversham and Fordwich, also then a port, near Canterbury. A Cinque Ports 'cesse' or tax for shipping made in Elizabeth I's reign, refers to a William Harris 'cessed at five shillings'.

This Harris connection with Fordwich, through the Cinque Ports, is also a strong indication that Richard Harris is interred in St. Mary the Virgin church, Fordwich, although it might be thought Teynham church, close to his cherry orchards, would be more appropriate. In the floor of St. Mary's is a brass inscribed: 'Mistress Harris died 1570. The wife of the Queenes Maiestes fruiterer.' If she was the wife of Richard and not the 'cessed' William then it is possible Richard was also buried there,

The primary school and old cherry orchard in Station Road, Teynham in 1984.
Between the trees can be seen the housing estate that was built on the site of New
Gardens.

perhaps with Mistress Harris.

Being taxed for shipping indicates the Harris family's vessels used the
Cinque Ports of Faversham and Fordwich, almost certainly sending crops
out from them. Teynham was ideally situated to have its fruit transported
by wagon to Faversham and Conyer from where sailing craft could take
it to London where the food markets had to meet the demands of an
increasing population. It is unlikely that the entire Harris fruit production
would be solely for the monarch and the court – they would need to sell
the surplus elsewhere .

Richard Harris would have known about the earlier cultivation of cherries on the estate lands of the manor of Teynham and so be aware that
both the soil and climate of the area were suitable for them. A local tradition is that the area known as New Gardens was given to Harris by Henry
VIII for additional cherry cultivation.

This has been contested and it is claimed that the area now Osier Farm,
Teynham, near the present stream, was first planted with cherry trees by

Harris and they produced a sufficient crop to encourage him to plant more – on the New Gardens area. The manor rolls refer to New Gardens as Brenithe, Brenyth or Brennet, the name used by Lambarde in 1570. They also contain a note stating that 'Ozier's Farm' was The Brennet, thus strengthening the case for Osier Farm being the first site planted by Harris. What is now New Gardens was originally called the Teynham Outlands because the area was an outlying part of the archbishop's manor.

If New Gardens was the second area Harris planted with cherry trees it would have been an appropriate name. It seems likely the area now Osier Farm, the land north and east of it, and New Gardens, to the southwest, were all part of the estate reputedly given to Harris and cherries were planted on each of them.

Seventeenth century expansion

There was an expansion of cherry cultivation from Teynham into other suitable areas of Kent in a relatively short time allowing for the planting of the trees and for them to reach a fruit-bearing age. By the first quarter of the seventeenth century it was the foremost county in England for fruit cultivation, of which cherries and apples were the prime fruits.

At the end of the century cherries were already growing in areas where they still grew within living memory. Hall and Russell, in their *Report on Agriculture and Soils in Kent* of 1911, state: The cultivation of fruit is very definitely located and is only carried on to any extent on certain special soils. The fruit area forms a band starting out from the southeast of London and following the belt of free-working loams on the Thanet Sands and the Chalk as far as the Medway Valley.

'The Medway Valley forms the nucleus of another area; a large proportion of the land on the Lower Greensand on either side of the valley west of Maidstone is in fruit and here the acreage increases every year on the higher lands at the expense of hops. When the Medway Valley opens out in the Weald Clay plain fruit still follows its course on the alluvial soil and even on to the sands and clays of the High Weald, though as soon as the Greensand has been passed the fruit no longer forms the leading feature in the landscape.

'East of the Medway Valley one of the richest areas of fruit land is formed by the deep loams of the Thanet Sands, Chalk and Brick Earth, which stretch from Rochester through Sittingbourne to Canterbury, while beyond Canterbury fruit continues to follow the outcrop of the Thanet Sands through Wingham and Wickham round to Ash and Sandwich. In the main it will be seen that fruit and hops run together; indeed the same grower is very often deep in both crops; fruit, however, prefers the lighter soils and so extends on the Thanet Sands closer to London.

'East Kent resembles Mid-Kent in its orchards save that nuts are rarely seen and the cherry plays a leading part instead. . . successful cherry growing seems to demand a substratum of chalk; unless the soil is somewhat calcareous and is also naturally well drained the cherry dies or fails before reaching maturity.'

The first large acreage put to cultivating cherries was that between Rainham, in the west, along the Medway estuary and North Downs, to Faversham in the east and south of Sittingbourne and Faversham, again there being, along this belt, an access to numerous quays – at Milton, Rainham, Otterham, Upchurch, Lower Halstow, Conyer and elsewhere – for taking the fruit surplus to local and regional sale, or by sea to London.

Soon added was the area around Gravesend, Dartford and up to the boundary of what is now east London, the fruit here being transported to the capital from wharves at Gravesend, Erith and Woolwich. In her *Journeys,* made in Kent in 1697, Celia Fiennes wrote: 'I went to Gravesend which is all by the side of cherry grounds that are of several acres of ground and run quite down to the Thames.' She refers to them being 'Kentish cherries, a good sort of Flemish fruit'.

The area around Canterbury and eastwards of the city, on the Maidstone to Ashford ridge, in the Medway valley and the Mid-Kent belt, south and southwest of Maidstone, also became cherry growing areas in the nineteenth century, followed by some orchard extension into the Low Weald.

Daniel Defoe, in *A Tour Through England and Wales,* written in 1725, says: 'Maidstone . . . round this town are the largest cherry orchards and the most of them that are in any part of England; and the gross of the quantity of cherries and the best of them which supply the whole city of London come from hence and are therefore called Kentish cherries.

'From the country adjoining Maidstone also is a very great quantity of

Now extinct Kent Black pigs in a cherry orchard, c 1911. Note the greasebands round the trunks of the trees.

corn brought up to London, besides hops and cherries. . . Also very great quantities of fruit, such as Kentish pippins, runettes, etc., which come up as the cherries do, hoy loads at a time to the wharf called the Three Cranes, in London.'

The majority of these early cherry orchards or gardens as they were also called, were between two to five acres in extent although there were exceptions. An orchard at Crayford covered nine acres and no doubt there were even larger ones.

In 1651 Samuel Hartlib, a writer on husbandry, describes how the cherry and apple orchards he knew were organised for cultivation. The trees were grown in rows twenty to thirty feet apart each way, the land in between down the avenues and the crosswork being ploughed and planted with crops, usually corn. Sometimes soft fruit or hops in hop growing areas were grown as alternative to corn, the hops being grown to two to three years until the cherry trees had achieved some growth.

When the cherry trees were tall and mature enough, so the branch spread produced sufficient fruit, the growing of crops in between the tree rows ceased and grass was sown as pasture for sheep and sometimes heifers. So the grassed orchard came into existence and remained a feature of Kent's cherry orchards well into the present century.

The grassed orchard had several advantages, one being that in drought summers the grass remained sufficiently green and lush for the livestock. It grew earlier in springtime in the orchard than in the open pasture, and the trees provided some shelter for the animals. In some orchards the grass may have had a slight dwarfing effect on the trees, checking growth as the season advanced by drawing on the soil moisture. This would cause them to develop short-jointed, fruit-bearing spurs instead of coarse outgrowths or wet wood, also known as 'waterwood'.

Another benefit of grass is that it dries the soil surface and absorbs the water from an average rainfall as the cherries are ripening. If the trees had to take up the rainfall rapidly, the cherries would split.

The livestock were removed, when the trees were washed, to avoid chemical contamination and allowed back when any chemicals absorbed by the grass had dissipated. They were taken away again as the fruit ripened and it was necessary to bring in ladders and prepare the orchards for picking. However, I have picked in orchards where the sheep were kept in to keep the grass down and have had to keep a sharp eye open on chips full of picked cherries otherwise the sheep would help themselves.

The ideal rule was to stock twelve sheep to the acre in summer and six in winter, but these numbers could only be carried in some orchards by artificial feeding with roots and hay in winter, corn and cake in summer. In this way the rich dung maintained the fertility of the soil for the trees although sometimes in a wet summer the grass would grow faster than this number of sheep could keep it reduced.

It was also customary to move sheep off exposed areas, such as Romney Marsh, into the cherry orchards of East Kent in autumn until blossom time – to the mutual advantage of sheep farmer and cherry grower.

According to Hartlib, if the grass was too rank and sour for sheep and cattle it was still of use for running hogs. Kent Black Pigs were still being run in poor producing, declining cherry orchards in the early years of this century. Frequently geese, sometimes even goats, were run on the grass to keep it so it resembled a lawn.

That other intrepid rural traveller, William Cobbett, in his *Rural Rides,* 1820, comments on the methods of cultivation he saw when visiting the hop gardens and fruit orchards then existing from Maidstone to Mereworth:

'This is what the people of Kent call the Garden of England. It is a district of meadows, cornfields, hop gardens and orchards of apples, pears, cherries and filberts, with very little if any land which cannot, with propriety, be called good. . . The culture is sometimes mixed; that is to say, apple trees or cherry trees or filbert trees and hops, in the same ground. This is a good way, they say, of raising an orchard. I do not believe it and I think that nothing is gained by any of these mixtures.

'They plant apple trees or cherry trees in rows here; then they plant a filbert tree close to each of these large fruit trees and then they cultivate the middle of the ground by growing potatoes. This is being too greedy. It is impossible that they can gain by this. What they gain one way they lose the other way and I believe that the most profitable way would be never to mix things at all.'

The front of New Gardens House, Teynham in 1948. *Photo: Alan Wilcox, Rainham.*

19

Despite Cobbett's critical comments and whether he was right or not, the practice of growing several crops in this manner in the vicinity of each other continued in Kent until well into the first quarter of the present century and was revived at the outset of the Second World War. Then the land in between rows of small fruit trees was used to grow potatoes and other low crops. The practise has now apparently ceased.

Cherry gardens

It seems a particular Kentish whim for certain types of crops to be grown in 'gardens'. Sheila Kaye-Smith suggests in her *Weald of Kent and Sussex,* that hops and cherries were said to grow in gardens and not in fields because tithes were claimed from fields but not from gardens. Obviously it made economic sense for farmers to describe their cultivated acres as gardens rather than fields – although tithes were certainly imposed on the acreages of hops, whether growing in a hop garden or hop field.

The early writers on Kent refer to its cherry gardens and its apple orchards. Eventually the use of garden for cherry cultivation declined and orchard was used for cherries, too.

The use of this term 'cherry garden', however, has made it possible to trace the spread of cherry cultivation after Harris's plantings at Teynham. When the name survives for a place, farm, cottage, road or street, this indicates the site of a cherry cultivation although the last cherry tree there may have been removed long ago.

There is a reference in Canterbury City Archives to an early example of the name 'cherry garden' being applied to an area of land. In a law case in 1562 William Stephen sued Anthony Moswell concerning a parcel of land, approximately six acres in extent in the parish of St. Dunstan and of Harbledown, formerly called Brusshe Elms but, at the date stated, known as The Cherry Garden. Whether the land was supporting cherry trees in 1562 or had even by then been cleared of them is unknown, but the name remained.

In 1706 a tenement in St. Dunstan's parish, Canterbury, was still known as The Cherry Garden, although sometimes called Stone Hall, according to the churchwardens accounts. Another undated, but believed to be earlier entry in the accounts, mentions 'The Cherry Garden next to the Bridewell, sometimes called The Stone Hall'. The name still survives for this modern residential district – Cherry Garden Road, Canterbury, and Cherry Garden Farmhouse which dates from about the seventeenth century.

Edward Hasted, in the second volume of *The History and Topographical Survey of the County of Kent,* mentions another early cherry orchard: 'From the London road the ground rises southward to the village of Swanscombe, at the west end of which is the mansion of the manor, much of which has been pulled down and it is now used as a farmhouse, and a little further the parsonage and church. Round the village there is some tolerable good land, though rather inclined to gravel and some orchard round: even so early as the 36th year of King Henry VIII mention is made in a grant of it, of an orchard here, called the Cherry Garden, belonging to the mansion of the manor.'.

New Gardens cherry orchard

The house that originally stood on the site of New Gardens House, Teynham, was reputed to have been built by Richard Harris. It was at one time in the possession of the Roper family who became the Lords Teynham and they sold it and the land in 1714 to Sir Robert Furnese of Waldershare, Kent. Subsequently it descended to one of his daughters, the Countess of Rockingham, who after the death of her first husband, married the Earl of Guilford. It stayed in the possession of that family until bought from them by Colonel James Honeyball, formerly Commanding Officer of the East Kent Volunteers, and an expert agriculturist and hop grower.

In the lifetime of the Countess of Rockingham the property had consisted of the farm, two large barns, two stables, one granary, one lodge, twenty acres of land, arable and pasture, one old cherry orchard and two acres of hop ground. It was in a neglected state when Colonel Honeyball purchased it and set about restoring the house, farm and gardens but so notable did the estate and New Gardens House become that George VI, when Duke of York, visited it on 14 July 1922. To mark the occasion the gravelled drive and some of the grounds were decorated with white roses as a compliment to the House of York.

Colonel Honeyball died in 1923 and his widow continued to run the estate and house and opened the gardens to the public on Sundays in spring and summer.

Mrs Honeyball showed visitors around the gardens and sometimes took them to a part of the cherry orchard that ran from near the house northwards almost to the railway line and told them this was the area where the first cherry trees were planted by Harris. After her death she was buried with her husband in the family vault in Teynham churchyard. In the church there is a plain brass tablet in memory of James Frederick Honeyball of New Gardens, the last owner.

The empty house was badly vandalised and became near derelict. It was demolished after the Second World War and the orchards cleared for development as a housing estate.

3

CHERRY ORCHARD TRADITIONS

EACH YEAR, on a Sunday early in May when the cherry blossom is at its best, a ceremony known as Blessing the Cherry Orchard took place as part of Evensong in some of the cherry growing areas of Kent.

The vicar and churchwardens, accompanied by the robed choir preceded by the Crucifix, and followed by the entire church congregation, would process from the local church to a neighbouring orchard. A short prayer was said, then the vicar blessed the orchard, after which the procession reformed and, singing the Litany, all walked back to the church for Evensong. Within living memory this ceremony took place at Newington-by-Sittingbourne.

The Blessing the Orchard is an adaption of an ancient rural custom during the church's season of Rogationtide. In Rogation week fields and other areas of cultivation were blessed to promote the newly sown crops and protect them from harmful influences. It had its origin in pagan times, and was one of the seasonal fertility rites adapted by the early Christians.

In the Victorian, but less so in the Edwardian period, it was a practice in some areas of Kent to impose the payment of 'shoe money' on cherry pickers. In my experience in the orchards around Rainham during the 1940s to 1960s, however, I never saw or heard of 'shoe money' being paid and it is safe to say that in this area at least the practice, if it had ever existed, had died out by that time.

A possible reason for its omission is that we who picked these orchards were all locals. We lived at home and went to the orchards in the evenings after work, at weekends, or as part of a holiday from our usual job to earn extra money. We were paid at the end of each week until the cherry season was finished. Then we collected our final money and were finished until the next cherry season, unless, of course, we went on to apple and pear picking.

The imposition of 'shoe money' had been common for generations in the Kent hop picking areas where the pickers lived in huts for the season.

Within living memory the Blessing of the Cherry Orchard ceremony was held at Newington-by-Sittingbourne church. *Photo: Tony Blake Collection.*

Milstead church, set amid the cherry orchards south of Sittingbourne.

If non-regular pickers or 'foreigners' visited a hop garden, usually to meet and help relatives and friends with their picking, their shoes or boots were wiped with a bundle of hop bines or an old hop-stained apron. After this the visitors were expected to pay their 'shoe money' or 'footing' as it was alternatively called.

If they failed to contribute some money they were pushed or lifted into a large hop basket or a hop bin and kept there until they paid up. The cash collected was used either to pay for beer at the evening meal or, more usually, it was saved up to spend on bread, cheese, cake and beer for the pickers' feast on the last day of the hopping season,

The custom of wiping the shoes and boots of visitors with some twigs of cherry leaves was probably more common in cherry orchards close to hop gardens picked by east London pickers and 'foreigners'.

Cherry picking

Cherry growing and picking have their own special words. The season of gathering the cherries was known in the growing districts as 'cherrying'. Similarly in these and other different fruit growing districts fruit picking was known as 'fruiting'.

The orchards were picked in several ways depending on the acreage of each plantation of trees, their height and maturity. The varieties did not all ripen at the same time, by design, so the early varieties were picked first, then mid-season and ending with late varieties.

It was usually the practice for women, who were often the faster pickers, to pick in a gang, with one, two or three women per tree depending on its size. Each gang had its own farm man as ladder mover or setter. It was his job to set each ladder safely in a tree for the women to pick from. He would move them around the tree to different settings and, when the tree was picked, move the ladders to trees still to be picked.

The women placed great reliance on their regular ladder mover and were not so confident when, for some reason or other, he was replaced by someone else. Some of the ladder movers also weighed the half-sieves or chips of cherries to check each contained its correct weight and quantity, and would also fetch empty baskets or chips to be filled and generally ensured the women had all they needed to continue picking without hindrance.

A group of women cherry pickers, with their children, in the Faversham area, *c* 1910. The flat rungs and their pegs can clearly be seen on the tapered ladders.

The men picked alone – one per tree or perhaps a father and son or sons, or two or three brothers or friends – again the number per tree depending on its size and quantity of fruit. The men moved their own ladders and fetched and carried for themselves, except when the next plantation to be picked was a considerable distance away. Then the ladders were put on horse-drawn carts and later tractor-hauled trailers.

The farm man, who was sometimes the farm manager, weighed the men's fruit, booked it to the picker, then loaded it on the cart or trailer and took it to the farm. In my time 'cherrying' women tended to pick the smaller tree plantations or younger orchards, whereas the men picked the older plantations and larger trees, sometimes as high as or higher than the average house, as well as smaller trees. But not always.

Although most women pickers did not like picking the very high trees there were some intrepid women – not necessarily those of masculine character – who did climb and pick such trees as well as any man. In the Victorian and Edwardian days large tree varieties were much more commonly cultivated and women used to pick them as well as the smaller trees.

The setting or exact placing of a ladder in a tree near the unpicked fruit was important for reasons of safety. It had to be long enough to extend beyond the part of the tree against which it rested and a certain amount of strength and an experienced eye for just the right place for a setting was needed.

The ladder was levered into the tree sideways on, then turned on to the setting so that it faced inwards. Sometimes, with a long ladder, the mover would run half way up it to ensure it was set safely for whoever was to use it. If setting his own ladder the picker took the responsibility for its safety.

The older, high cherry trees were notoriously awkward for setting ladders compared with

The author picking at Callaway Brothers Platters Farm, Rainham in 1964. Note how the ladder is set in a fork of a branch.

apple trees which have numerous thick, fruit-bearing branches. The cherry tends to have thin, weak branches with outward extensions of drooping masses of leafy twigs or, as with the variety Victoria Black, massive trunks with enormously thick lower branches growing upwards at an

27

angle so there were virtually no sides to pick – the fruit being mainly at the top.

The ladder, in such cases, would be set with only its narrow top against the twiggy mass. It would be almost upright so that some of the picker's weight would be extended down the ladder to the ground. As the picker climbed higher the ladder head would move into the top of the tree and some of the picker's weight was then against the setting.

When setting a ladder against a cherry tree's branches and twigs the rule was to place it so that should it slip it would fall towards the trunk. Whenever possible there would be a secondary setting lower down or further into the tree so that if the ladder slipped from the primary setting it would come to rest against the second.

Settings occasionally did give way, with the result that the ladder moved through or out of the tree throwing the picker off and causing injury or even death. Most pickers have had a ladder fall in or out of a tree and when it happens, as I know from personal experience, it is not pleasant.

The advice given to pickers was – if you feel the ladder slipping and think you have time, climb down it or jump off when near the ground. However, if picking at or near the top, it is best to grip a ladder rung within both hands and hold on tightly until it stops going through the tree. If it does not stop, jump off just before it hits the ground.

A joke among pickers was: 'If the ladder falls through a tree don't waste time but pick the cherries you pass on your way down.'

4

TOOLS AND TERMS OF THE TRADE

SPECIAL ladders, often made locally, were used in Kent orchards. They were strong, but light enough to be carried upright and were more tapered and slender in their length than ones used by thatchers, tilers and builders.They were three foot wide at the foot and narrowed to about twelve inches at the top. Being 'bottom heavy' the ladders were easier to move; had more stability for use in cherry trees offering poor settings; and allowed the pickers to lean a considerable distance to either side away from the ladder without it slipping sideways.

A ladder's length was indicated by the number of its rungs – twenty five, thirty five, forty, fifty– to a maximum of sixty five. The sides were of sweet chestnut, pine or spruce, if available, and were cut by sawing lengthwise down one straight tree of the required height and diameter.

The inner faces of both lengths were planed flat, but the curved outer face was, at this stage, left covered with its bark.The two sides were positioned together and, at intervals of nine inches apart, marks were made for the holes for the rungs and these were drilled with a tapered auger.

Seasoned oak, or beech was used for the rungs, each of which was roughly cleft with a draw-shave and then rounded with a plane or in a lathe. There were also a number of flat-sided rungs, each three inches in depth, at intervals up the length of a ladder, and across the foot as the first rung. These 'flats', unlike the rounded rungs, projected through cuts in the sides and were held in position with pegs. Rungs and flats were left outside to weather and dry thoroughly so that after assembly they would not shrink and become loose.

Making up was done by placing one side, outer bark face down, on two or three trestles, depending on the length required, and putting the rungs and flats in the holes drilled and cut for them, starting with the widest flat at the foot.

The flats would be positioned between the rungs at six or seven rung intervals to give the ladder strength and keep it tight, and all knocked in with a mallet. The flat face of the second side was then put over the ends

The length of these ladders gives some idea of the height of the 'open sided' trees the women are picking in this Kent orchard at the turn of the century. *Photo: Neil Mattingly*

Pictured left, with the scales and trays full of cherries, is a kibsy basket with the leather belt by which it was worn round the picker's waist.

30

of the rungs and flats. Two men, one each end, would hold the side while a third eased the ends of the rungs and flats into place and knocked the side on with a mallet. Rungs that protruded through the holes in the sides were planed level and the flats had their corners removed with a draw shave. The bark, which had been kept on during the knocking in of the rungs and flats to absorb any misplaced mallet blows, was then planed off.

In the 1920s the cherry ladder was improved by E G Aylett, a ladder-maker and wheelwright of Bredgar. He used iron rods, known as tie bolts, at six or seven rung intervals on his ladders. These bolts were pushed through holes in the sides and a nut placed on the threaded end and tightened against a shaped washer.

The intention was to give extra strength to Aylett's ladders, which he patented under Patent No 108638. Two other notable makers of cherry ladders were Gilbert and Son of Rainham and Howard Brunger of Chilham.

Cherry language

The terms a 'light' or 'heavy' setting was indirectly concerned with weight, but more so with quantity. A heavy setting was one where each branch and twig was bearing a large quantity of sound, ripe fruit – a light setting was one where the fruit was sparse, or small in size, or both. The former was obviously a better earner of money as the baskets could be filled more quickly and less time was spent moving the ladder around the tree

'Scrumps' were small cherries previously left hanging on the trees because they were unripe. A 'scrump' was also a stunted apple. I picked for a certain cherry grower at Rainham who, if there was still a demand from the London hotels at the end of the cherry season, would pay his pickers by the hour, instead of by the number of chips, to go 'scrumping' over the entire orchard gathering whatever ripe cherries they could find. The cherries would all be mixed in together and sent direct to the hotels. One wonders with what high-sounding name they appeared on the hotel menus?

In areas around Sittingbourne this task was known as 'middling'. It is often the case that cherries in the middle of a tree, close to the trunk, are unripe or green and small, while elsewhere on the tree they are ripe for picking. If, later on, a good price was still obtainable, the pickers would be paid to go around the orchard to pick all the 'middlings', which by then were ripe.

The stalk of the pendant cherry, that bears the f ruit and by which it is attached to the twig, is known as the 'strig'. To pull the cherry fruit from its strig accidentally was known as 'strigging' them or 'to strig' them. In other areas it was alternatively known as 'plumming' them. Cherries had to be picked for market with the strig attached. If it was torn from the cherry the fruit would quickly bruise and go bad.

Eddie Barton, formerly of Borden and with many years experience in fruit growing, told me his father had to explain to some of the families who came down from east London for the season that the cherries must be picked with their strigs. To which one of the men replied: 'What! guvnor. You want them with their handles on?'

The 'brut' or 'bruts' on a cherry twig is a leaf or flower-bearing shoot or shoots. To 'brut a tree' is when sheep nibble off young shoots on the low-hanging branches or a picker accidentally breaks off the shoots, leaves and fruit, usually when setting or removing a ladder.

The Kent word probably derived from the French *brout*, a shoot of young wood, and *brouter*, to nibble off such shoots. Some brutting is inevitable but clumsy pickers who do a lot of it are not looked upon kindly by growers.

Cherries were picked with both hands into a basket known as a 'kibsy' or 'kipsy'. It had a handle over the top by which to carry it when full, and one flat side that rested against the lower back when the basket was secured around the waist by a belt or thick cord.

How it was worn can be clearly seen in the picture, left, of the author's brother, Andre, picking cherries at Platters Farm, Rainham in 1964.

A party of cherry pickers in the Yalding area in 1917 – complete with ladder movers, baskets, cherries and babies. *Photo: Ray Baldock*

Some pickers preferred not to wear the kibsy but used an iron hook to suspend it in front of them from a rung on the ladder. The kibsy basket I used contained, when full, about 12 lbs of cherries. However, old photographs of men and women picking in the past show two, possibly three, different sizes of kibsy.

Another necessary item for picking, particularly of varieties such as Florence which had long, sweeping branches with cherries along their length, was the cherry hook. It was three feet or so long, had a hook at both ends and was made by the local blacksmith. It was used to pull the just out of reach branches closer to the picker. Many pickers, however, made their own S-shaped hooks from any length of metal rod that could be bent.

What to wear.

In the recent past no special clothes were worn by pickers but it was advisable to wear strong-soled shoes or boots to support the feet, otherwise much standing on the rounded ladder rungs made the insteps, ankles and lower leg muscles ache.

Headgear of all sorts, including a traditional woman agricultural worker's sunbonnet, was sported by the pickers – and a bearded mandolin player – at Copton Farm, near Faversham around 1914

If a rain shower occurred all manner of apparel materialised from holdalls and bags to keep the picker reasonably dry, from sou-westers that had never seen the sea and other forms of headgear, to plastic macs, ancient overcoats and oilskin jackets and trousers. If only a brief shower shelter was taken where it could be found – perhaps under a leafy tree, or sometimes there was a store shed in the orchard or a canvas tarpaulin on poles beneath which the picked cherries were placed.

After a shower the wind would blow the rainwater off the fruit and foliage and sometimes the sun would come out to aid the drying process. When it looked as if the rain had set in for the rest of the day picking ceased, not only to stop the pickers getting wet through but because cherries should not be picked when wet for a variety of reasons.

If the orchard had been disc-harrowed to get more nitrogen into the soil to improve the trees the mud on the ground after heavy rain would be transferred from the pickers shoes to the rungs of their ladders, making them slippery and muddy. The mud also got on the hands that held the rungs and ladder sides and from them to the fruit being picked, making it dirty.

In earlier days the women, in particular, dressed differently. Many wore long, often almost ankle-length aprons over thick skirts and blouses or full length dresses. Surprisingly these aprons were often white at the start of the day, but it can be imagined how they ended it when the wearers were picking juicy black cherries.

The headgear was varied and included plain boaters, straw hats decorated with artificial flowers, flat caps, berets and sometimes in hot weather white sunbonnets with a flap to protect the back of the neck from the sun.

At midday or thereabouts it was dinnertime, although if they had started early in the morning there would be a break in picking sometime around 9am–10am for some form of refreshment. Lunch for our generation was likely to have been cheese, spam, fish or meat paste sandwiches brought in a plastic box or tin. When picking ended, in the late afternoon or early evening, there would be a proper meal waiting for us when we got home

In earlier days no doubt whatever was on hand at home was

Women tied their hair up in headscarves in the 1940s

taken to the orchard, in a basket, a box, or spotted handkerchief.

There was also, of course, the cherries that somehow came off the strigs to eat, unless the crop being picked was of acid cooking, canning or dye cherries. Liquid refreshment for us was a flask of tea, a fruit drink or beer. For our forebears it would have been cold tea, milk, flat lemonade or cider for the women, and cold tea, cider or beer for the men.

More pictures from the author's family album – his three year old daughter,
Stephanie, guarding, and eating, three chips of Bradbourne Black cherries
and below, left to right, the pickers with full baskets are Percy Major,
Platters Farm manager Alf Harris, and Bert Strevens.

5

OFF TO MARKET

CHERRIES were sent to market in light, flat bottomed 'chip' baskets, with metal carrying handles. Each contained 12 lbs of fruit and a card bearing the name of the grower, recipient and variety, was fitted flat under the handle but over the cherries to cover them.

Previously cherries had been transported in much sturdier half-sieve baskets, containing a half-bushel – 28 lbs. They had rounded sides and a flat bottom so they could be stacked one on top of the other when sent by rail fruit van or by lorry. These baskets were first lined with thick blue packing paper to protect the fruit and covered with a circle of more blue packing paper labelled with the grower's name, address, sometimes the fruit variety, and its destination. The packing paper was kept in position by lengths of hazel twig fitted either crosswise or lengthwise over it to hold it in place.

This method of transporting cherries had gone out of use when I was cherrying in North Kent in the 1950s and 1960s but the baskets survived for many years and were used for other purposes. That this basket method was not always a satisfactory way of getting the fruit to market in an unblemished, reasonably good condition is indicated by the comments of such earlier authorities as Hall and Russell.

In their 1911 *Report* they say: 'Kentish fruit is usually packed in round bushel (hard fruit – apples and pears) and half bushel (cherries) baskets, called 'sieves' and 'half-sieves', but though the fruit travels well in these baskets their appearance is not particularly taking. Indeed, as regards packing and grading the Kentish fruit grower is much behind his foreign competitors and fails to do justice to his wares'.

Later, in his *A Pilgrimage of British Farming*, Hall went even further. He not only blamed the growers for continuing to use returnable baskets and packing the fruit in them so tightly that it suffered bruising, but he also accused the South Eastern Railway of inefficiency.

'Of the adventures of returned empties on the South Eastern Railway many lurid tales are told of search parties taking the line, section by section, of submerged trucks full of baskets that wash up in distant stations and there lie stranded in the sidings, but such is the face of long custom that the Kentish grower has not yet been converted to the value of non-returnable packages, which neither bring back disease nor mean idle capital', he wrote.

In spite of such criticism cherries continued to be despatched to Covent Garden market and elsewhere in half-sieve baskets until the late 1930s. Eventually the non-returnable 12lb chip combined with transport by lorry, direct from grower to market, solved the problems Hall and Russell referred to.

6

BIRDS, INSECTS AND OTHER NATURAL HAZARDS

IN late April and May cherry orchards are a mass of foamy white blossoms – a scene of beauty to visitor and country dweller. The grower is hoping there will be no frosts to damage the blossom. Most cherries were, and still are, bought at auction sales from growers when at the fruit stage, but there were occasionally private sales of cherries when the trees were in blossom.

This was a high risk transaction for the buyer as frost, hail, and other vagaries of the weather could damage the trees before the cherries were at the fruit stage. There is a Kent saying: 'Dry May, no hay, plenty of cherries', for in dry air conditions the pollen will scatter and pollinate. In moist air conditions it sticks and does not do so. Cold air, like water, flows down Kentish Downland slopes on a clear night, settling in the flatter valley of fields and orchards below and creating frost pockets.

Growers, when they were able to, avoided these areas when planning their new orchards, but if the soil was suitable for cherry trees they were likely to take the risk. Another peril was a series of cold winds in May. They would cause the young fruit to shrivel and drop from the twigs. A hailstorm could also ruin cherries by making brown marks on them and pitting them.

On one occasion in the 1930s the cherry auctions had just ended and the orchards of ripening cherries been sold when a violent hailstorm hit the Hartlip-Stockbury area and so badly damaged the crop that not a cherry could be picked and the buyers sustained a huge financial loss.

When cherries are ripening success or failure depends a great deal on whether there is heavy rainfall. If there is the cherries are likely to split open, exposing the interior flesh, and go bad. Split cherries are unsaleable.

A cherry, depending on its variety, takes in a quantity of water from the tree via its stalk and rainfall by absorption through its skin. If there is a rapid intake of water by a tree laden with maturing cherries the likely result is that the fruit will be unable to take in even more water and consequently the skin will split. Fortunately the varieties in orchards mature at different stages during the season so not all will be affected by heavy rainfall. However it would be financially disastrous for the grower if it rained throughout the season and all varieties were affected.

Some varieties seem less susceptible to cracking than others, possibly because they absorb less water through the skin, which is glossy smooth so some of the rain runs off.

The orchard's water table can affect the quantity the trees take from it, influencing the water content of the cherries. As previously mentioned the grass floor of a cherry orchard absorbs rain when cherries are close to maturity, but even the grass cannot absorb all the water from prolonged heavy rain. It was quickly realised by early cherry growers it was preferable to plant their trees in areas of low rainfall.

Another natural hazard is birds. Wood pigeons, jays, blackbirds and thrushes are all attracted to the fruit but the worst marauders are starlings, especially when combined into flocks of hundreds, perhaps thousands. While picking the pickers would hear the swish of wings passing overhead, followed by a rain of droppings on the leaves. The chattering starlings would descend on a part of the orchard awaiting picking and in a short time would wreak havoc on the crop.

Starlings among cherries are voracious and destructive, pecking in all directions, spoiling more than they eat, messing the crop and stripping trees. They will pluck at a cherry and if they drop it, pluck at another and so on without pause. When disturbed the starlings rise as a black cloud and wheel away to another area of the orchard and continue their damage. It is incredible, afterwards, to see how the birds have also stripped the flesh from the stone, which is left hanging on its strig. Sometimes complete clusters of what had been ripening cherries only remain as stones on strigs.

Wood pigeons will fill their crop with cherries and fly away. Blackbirds and thrushes consume cherries but the quantity of their predation is not significant.

Scaring tactics have been adopted against starlings and pigeons. One that survived into the 1930s, perhaps later, was to send a lad, often as his first farm job, to walk or run around the orchards shouting and whirring hand rattles or wooden clappers, shaking stones in a tin, or banging two noise-making objects against each other to set up a sudden din.

Another method involved a man with the double-barrelled shotgun. He was sometimes of an age past active cherry picking, but younger men were also employed as human bird scarers. They moved around the orchards periodically firing their shotguns especially if starlings were about. Black powder scare cartridges were used for maximum noise effect to keep the starlings on the move and another noise method was the firework-like scarer comprising a length of treated rope with bangers at spaced intervals. These were suspended from tree branches and lit at the bottom, the rope smouldering upwards to ignite banger after banger.

Another method was to hang sheets of corrugated iron and old pots, pans, large tins and similar objects strung together from a strong branch by a length of rope. Every so often a farm lad or anyone walking through the orchard would tug the end of the rope, pulling the pots and pans away from the corrugated iron and then letting them fall back onto it with an almighty crash. Such assemblages of metal were scattered throughout the orchard to scare the birds.

Among other scaring devices were bright orange balloons and kites, some in the shape of hovering birds of prey, which would be flown above the orchard tree tops. Still in use is the static automatic 'gun' that 'fires' repeatedly at a set time. This has the required effect of scaring the birds but does not please every human living within earshot.

Diseases of the cherry

Disease damage and insect predation is something else the grower has to face. Cherry trees can be affected by 'silver leaf', which causes the foliage to take on a silvery or leaden appearance on some branches. Unless dealt with this fungus will eventually kill the tree.

The treatment in the past was to saw off the affected branches back to healthy wood and paint the cut with white lead paint to seal it. This had to be done after July because if removed too early globular lumps of sticky gum would ooze out of the cut and could cause gummosis, making the tree unhealthy, killing the rest of the branch and eventually the tree.

Cherry trees also suffer with leaf scorch – a fungus which causes the leaves to develop yellow patches, have a scorched appearance and wither.

The treatment in the past was to collect and burn all the fallen leaves, and take off all those still hanging on the tree. The modern way is to spray the affected tree with a fungicide before the buds open.

Another insect pest is the cherry blackfly. The young leaves and shoots become distorted, growth is checked, and the foliage becomes coated with sticky honeydew and sooty mould. A tar oil winter wash will kill off the blackfly's overwintering eggs.

The cherry bark tortrix moth has caterpillars that live in colonies, bore into a tree's bark, moving round to encircle it totally, sometimes killing the tree if it is weak. Clues to its presence are rough swellings on the trunk or large branches.

A sight no longer seen in cherry and other fruit orchards is grease banded trees with their trunks wrapped around some five to seven feet from the ground with a bandage of paper, on which was spread a gummy compound. This trapped the wingless female winter moths as they attempted to crawl up the trunk to the branches and lay their eggs on the buds. The grease used for banding the trees came from the makers in cartons and drums ready prepared for use. It was spread on with some improvised tool such as a flat piece of wood. Sometimes women who cherry picked in the orchard were employed in autumn on this task.

One manufacturer was Abol Ltd., Paddock Wood, whose product in 1937, Stictite, smeared on to a length of greaseproof paper was claimed not to run, dry out or lose its tackiness during the season. It was available at various prices from ls 6d.(7½p) for half a pound .Ready prepared bands were also available at 2s 6d, (12½p) a carton and protected fifteen to twenty average sized trees.

Another tree banding was Orbite, from Kay Brothers, Reddish, who offered: 'a pail of 28lbs sufficient for 140 to 280 trees, at 44s 4d., delivered by makers to your nearest railway station at no extra charge.'

Other methods of combatting insects and disease were applied during the winter months when trees were leafless, preferably soon after leaf fall, and there were fewer tasks on the farm. They would be done on days when there was no strong wind, no risk of rain or frost. These methods usually consisted of coating the trees with a powder or performing what was known as 'washing' or spraying the trees with various preparations.

The powder was formerly thrown by hand. Ray Baldock of Five

Ashes, near Mayfield, a friend with many years experience working on Kent farms, told me that one of his employers, when a lad around 1914, had, with others, been employed in cherry orchards to throw a mixture of salt and lime up into the trees, using a domestic type coal shovel on a long handle to try and reach high into them. Usually this was done on damp, still days when the powder would, hopefully, cling to twigs and buds.

Washing cherry trees using hand held lances – for which the pay was sixteen shillings a day plus half a crown 'dirty money'.
Photo: Don Clark, Rainham.

Also at this time of year the farm lads had to scrape all the loose bark, moss and lichen off the trunks and lowest branches to reduce the hiding places for insect pests.

On the subject of keeping cherry trees healthy, Hall and Russell, in their 1911 *Report*, wrote: The trees are also kept clean by the regular practise of lime washing, which is being exchanged to an increasing extent now for the more effective caustic winter washes. Washing with arsenical preparations against caterpillars and with soft soap and quassia against aphis is very general: Bordeaux Mixture and other copper fungicides are now beginning to be used to combat scab, mildew and other diseases.'

The soft soap supposedly formed a film over the breathing tubes of aphids so they suffocated. Quassia was chips of the *Picrasma excelsa*, a tree related to the South American *Quassia amara*, which contains a bitter drug definitely not beneficial to aphids.

It was purchased as wood chips, or it arrived in quantity as cordwood in a van at the nearest railway station and taken by cart to the farm to be milled to chip size. The amount of chips boiled to extract the drug depended on the amount of insecticide required for spraying. For a gallon four ounces of chips would be boiled in that quantity of water, the liquid

43

was strained off and four ounces of soft soap added and thoroughly stirred in as the liquid cooled.

To combat caterpillars arsenate of lead was used as a spray. It was also mixed with lime sulphur and as one worker said to me: 'That was a stinking mixture if ever there was one'.

Bacterial canker was the severest problem in a cherry orchard. It occurred most frequently when the trees made too much soft growth a result of heavy rainfall or too much nitrogen. The spores entered the tree through wounds and unpainted cuts, affecting young shoots and causing 'dieback' or 'dead tip'. For this Bordeaux Mixture containing copper sulphate, quicklime or hydrated lime and water, was used or Burgundy Mixture made like Bordeaux but with washing soda instead of lime. Several applications were made as soon as the leaves had fallen to get a measure of control.

A universally used winter wash for fruit tree, including cherries, was tar oil, first introduced in the early 1920s. Horticulturists still know it as Mortegg produced by the Murphy Chemical Company in 1938, one gallon costing eight shillings. (40p), ten gallons 41s.6d. Another wash – it cost 7s 6d a gallon – was Abolene from Plant Protection of Yalding.

It was claimed one good saturation of tar oil sprayed on the trees so it reached into every fissure of bark and branches, twigs and buds, was more likely to destroy overwintering adult insects pests and their eggs and guard against various diseases, than any other treatment. Another advantage of the tar spray was that the grass beneath the trees was only browned for a short time and tar oil had no long term effect on it,

An insecticide used in powder form in the 1930s was one called Polvo. It was also highly efficacious at destroying wasps' nests in orchards and nearby hedgebanks. Before and after the Second World War another insecticide used was Nicotine Liquid, which according to the label on the tin was 'guaranteed 96 to 98 per cent pure'.

Long before engine-powered methods of tree spraying hand pumps were used to get the liquid into the trees. The wash, in a 120/150 gallon barrel, was taken to the orchard on a cart and then hand pumped, via hand-held hoses with metal lances fixed to their ends, on to tree branches and trunk. Lances were available for any type of tree wash and could reach a distance of about forty feet. However they did not give a fine

One of the pumps for tree washing in use at Jack Clark's Pump Farm, Rainham in 1958. *Photo: Don Clark, Rainham.*

enough mist effect for washes other than tar oil.

Another method of getting the spray to the trees was from a stationary pump via underground pipes leading to stand pipes at about six tree spacings apart. The men connected their hoses to a standpipe and sprayed the trees around it, then moved on to the next standpipe and repeated the operation.

Even into the late 1940s horsedrawn pumps were used in orchards. One, called a 'mistifier', was powered by a Lister engine driving a three-thrower set, that is a pump with three pistons. If the pump was in good condition and the hoses were not perished the pressure could be increased up to 400 psi. If the hoses did have a perished area then someone, not the tree, could suddenly get an unwelcome soaking.

Yet another method, for very high trees, was to have a man in a crow's nest mounted on a caterpillar-tracked vehicle, complete with engine and tanks of wash. While the man up aloft drenched the topmost branches with a hand-held jet, the men on the ground sprayed the lower branches and trunk, the jets being effective to a hundred or so feet, according to the pressure used. This was not the sort of equipment usually owned by the smaller fruit grower – only by those with a large acreage – so the former either hired it or employed a spray contractor to do the job.

The hand-held jet method of spraying was fairly labour intensive but eventually the operation became more and more mechanised.

These men washing trees in winter against insect damage have only old hats on their heads and nothing to protect the face from the insecticide.

When a fan was fitted to the rear of the tree-washing machine the wash was blown up through the trees and the whole process could be operated by one man.

This in turn was to be superceded by tree-washing machines with double fans at the rear, both capable of producing a 70mph gale that put the wash efficiently into and around most of the trees.

Tree washers were made, as part of their agricultural machine production by the now defunct firm of Weeks of Maidstone. Drake and Fletcher of Maidstone continues to make them.

7

SALES BY AUCTION AND SHOWS

HAVING avoided or overcome the many perils the cherry is prone to and achieved a substantial standard crop the grower might not want to pick all of it with his own pickers. He may choose to put the surplus up for sale by auction.

When the first cherry auctions began is not known but they were well established by the end of the nineteenth century when advertisements announcing the sales regularly appeared in local newspapers in May or June, before the fruit was ripe. In some years a thousand acres were up for disposal.

By the 1960s the Sittingbourne auction was one of the largest as a result of amalgamation in earlier years of smaller auctions held in North Kent.

A typical auction advertisement is this one from the *East Kent Gazette* of 25 June 1910:

> **CARPENTERS ARMS, EASTLING.**
> **FRUIT SALE.**
> Messrs. G.W. Finn beg to announce the Annual Sale of Cherries, Currants, etc., at the above Inn on Tuesday, 28th June, 1910, at six o'clock in the afternoon.

There then followed a long list of cherries and other fruit for auction and details of where the orchards and fields containing the crops were situated. Catalogues could be obtained from auctioneers or their agents and potential purchasers would visit the orchards to examine the fruit they were interested in buying and picking.

In due course reports of prices obtained appeared in the press. The *East Kent Gazette,* on 21 June, 1930 gave a lengthy report of cherry sales in the county. Of Sittingbourne Annual Cherry Sales conducted by F Austen Bensted and Sons at the Bull Hotel it recorded:

'There was a good attendance and smart competition. In the Borden orchards the outstanding example was that of F.C.Turner & Co., Northfield Orchard, Parsonage Farm, where 9 acres of cherries made £200, Mr Alfred Hinge being the buyer.

At Stockbury 9½ acres of cherries in Napoleon Orchard, Pett Farm, property of Mr Cecil Wright, made £335; they went to Mr S. Clinch. . .'

At P H Bishop's annual cherry sale in the Newington area, held at the Bull Hotel, the top price was £540 for seven and a half acres of cherries in Allen's Field, Rainham; at Hartlip two of L J Goodhew's orchards at Paradise Farm were sold, the cherries on the eight and three quarter acres on the east side making £220, and those on the six and a quarter acres on the west side, £170.

At another of P H Bishop's sales, this time in the Sittingbourne district, the cherries on E B Gascoyne's estate at Bapchild realised a total of £1,695, the top price of £525 being paid for ten acres of cherries in Tank Orchard.

Orchards were also sold at Newnham, Sheldwich, Bobbing, Milstead, Milton,Tonge, Rodmersham, Tunstall, Upchurch, Bredgar, Lynsted, which gives an idea of the extent of cherry growing in this area at that time.

Sixy five years later the *East Kent Gazette's* cherry auction price report of 21 June, 1995 showed a continuing decline in the trade:

'At the Sittingbourne and Boughton cherry sale 200 acres were on sale, realising £25,250, but fewer buyers in Boughton village hall. The top price was £6,000 obtained by cherries in Upper and Lower Wheat Field orchards, Rodmersham, for G. H. Dean and Co. Cherries in Soldier Bank orchard, Tonge, 15 acres, G. H. Dean, £2,900; cherries in Hooks Hole Orchard, Borden, 7.5 acres, F. T. Holt, £2,500. . .'

The buyer of the cherries would have to pick them with his own pickers and had the responsibility of marketing the crop. Hopefully he would make a profit providing there was no weather damage to the fruit or a drop in market prices.

In the past there were frequently people who wanted to be cherry growers for a season or so. They would buy a small orchard and perhaps have as an outlet a market stall or a local greengrocer's shop. Another possible customer could be a neighbouring grower of cherries who wanted to supplement his own, perhaps reduced, crop to sell on to his market connections.

Growers would have agents to sell their fruit for them on commission in London and other markets. These fruit salesmen/agents advertised for customers in newspapers in fruit growing districts.

In the *East Kent Gazette* in July 1890, a Robert Perry, 'established 1850, English Fruit and Flower Salesman of Smithfield Market, Manchester' begged to inform 'all growers of fruit, flowers and vegetables that he is open to receive large quantities of the above on commission. Having an extensive connection among the leading buyers he can command Fair Market Prices. Account Sales and Cheques Daily, Empty baskets, cases, labels, etc, supplied on request.'

Cherry shows

ALL the foremost growers in the past selected examples of their best quality fruit to exhibit in competition at cherry shows. Nowadays the

Judging at the Kent Soft Fruit Show at Maidstone in 1954. *Photo: John Topham*

place to see cherry varieties is in the cherry and soft fruit section of the Kent County Show held annually in July at Detling.

At this show there are usually between two to three dozen exhibitors with some two hundred entries of cherries and other fruit. Among the various awards for which they compete is the Fruiterers Company Medal; Sittingbourne, Faversham and District Growers Cup; the Sir Thomas Neame Memorial Salver; and the Peter Black Cup for Best Merton exhibit.

In accordance with tradition baskets of award winning varieties are presented to the reigning monarch and other members of the royal family. Today's recipients are the Queen, the Queen Mother and Princess Alexandra.

The cherry section of the Cherry and Soft Fruit Show at the Kent County Show at Maidstone in 1949. *Photo: NFU, South East Region.*

8

CULTIVATED CHERRIES

THE cherry is classed as a stone fruit, the stone being the rounded, smooth, woody shell enclosing the central kernel. The colour of the stone varied according to the variety, from pale yellow to that of the cherry's flesh – which would sometimes adhere to the stone.

The cherry is also divided into three types: the heart-shaped, sweet cherry; the round sweet cherry; and the sour cherry which is used for culinary purposes. An earlier classification divided them into 'foreign' heart-shaped Flemish or Flanders cherries imported from that country; and 'English' round-shaped varieties. Sweet cherries were further divided into 'hard' and 'tender' cherries, according to the consistency of their flesh.

The 'hard' cherries were the heart-shaped varieties with firm flesh; the 'tender' cherries the regular, round varieties with tender, watery flesh attached to the stone.

More than a thousand varieties have been named worldwide, but they may not all be different. There are many instances of a single variety having several different names according to locality. The practice of double and treble naming was more common in the past when nurseries added their own name to the same basic variety to increase sales. In 1938 the eminent nurserymen and tree suppliers, George Bunyard and Sons, Maidstone, had thirty seven different cherry varieties listed in their catalogue.

Sweet cherries

The majority of sweet cherry varieties will not set their fruit with their own pollen. The flowers must be fertilised by pollen of a different group variety. In an orchard or garden sweet cherry trees must at least be planted in cross-pollinating pairs.

The situation is further complicated because varieties of sweet cherries can also be in groups within which pollinations, even between different varieties, is not possible because of incompatibility. They need to be pollinated by compatible group varieties which produce flowers at the same time. There are, however, varieties which are cross-compatible and can be regarded as universal donors since they pollinate each other and possibly all others.

Varieties in the same group of sweet cherries, except the universal donors, should not be planted together but any variety may be planted with any other variety outside its own group provided they flower at the same time.

For example, Black Eagle fails with the pollen of Early Rivers, but it will fruit abundantly when pollinated by varieties in other groups. Alternatively, the pollen of Black Eagle cannot fertilise the flowers of Early Rivers but will do so with varieties in other groups.

Early Rivers is pollinated by Noir de Guben, Merton Heart. Florence by Kent Bigarreau and Merton Glory; Kent Bigarreau by Governor Wood, Merton Glory, Florence; Roundel by Frogmore, Governor Wood, Napoleon Bigarreau; Napoleon Bigarreau by Florence, Frogmore, Governor Wood, Roundel, Merton Glory.

The requirements of pollination entailed the cultivation of a considerable number of varieties in Kent. It is obviously necessary to plant a suitable selection of early, mid-season and late varieties so they are picked in succession through a season of three to five weeks. This century, however, for various commercial reasons, it has been the practice of cherry growers to plant fewer varieties and a larger number of each. In the older orchards it was usual to cultivate numerous varieties but comparatively few trees of each variety,

The two colour categories are Black – varying from near-black to dark wine-purple, the juice being 'black'; and White in which the skin and flesh can be pale yellow, pale pinkish-red, darker red, or sometimes yellow with pink streaks and the juice 'white' or colourless. The majority of sweet cherry varieties are for eating fresh and uncooked.

Sweet cherry varieties grown in Kent

Amber. An early white cherry cultivated in the county from the mid eighteenth century and recommended by Thomas Hitt in his *A Treatise of Fruit Trees.*

Black Eagle. A black cherry raised about 1806 by Elizabeth Knight,

52

daughter of Thomas Andrew Knight of Elton Hall, near Ludlow, by crossing Bigarreau with May Duke, same parent varieties as for Knights Early Black.

Bradbourne Black. Named after Bradbourne House, part of East Malling Research Station where it was developed. Large, heavy cropper..

Bullocks Heart. Heart shaped white but as it matures the skin takes on a Cherry Blossom brown appearance.

Early Rivers. Very early black variety raised from seed of Early Purple Guigne by Thomas Rivers, a Sawbridgeworth nurseryman. It was introduced in 1872 and quickly became the best quality early black variety in commercial cultivation. It is one of the few varieties whose fruits ripen in succession and the trees can be picked over two or three times, the first time to catch the early market. With other varieties it was usual to pick all the fruit in one go.

Elton Heart. Raised about 1806 by Thomas Andrew Knight at Elton Hall, near Ludlow, from Graffion pollinated by White Heart.

Florence. Late, usually the last variety to be picked. White, but the very sweet flesh tends to pinkish-red.

Frogmore Early. An early to mid-season white variety raised by Thomas Ingram, Queen Victoria's head gardener, at Frogmore, and introduced in 1864. A regular heavy cropper, following Early Rivers, commercially grown for London and other markets.

Gaucher Bigarreau. (Pronounced in the orchards Goy-shur). Black.

Governor Wood. Early to mid season; white. Originally an American cherry variety raised by a Professor Kirtland of Cleveland in 1842 and named after Reuben Wood, Governor of Ohio. Successful in Kent as a regular heavy cropper to rival Frogmore as a second early white variety.

Knights Early Black. Raised about 1810 by Thomas Andrew Knight from Bigarreau crossed with May Duke.

Merton Bigarreau. Early to mid-season; black. Raised by the John Innes Horticultural Institute in 1924 by crossing Knights Early Black with Napoleon Bigarreau. Susceptible to bacterial canker. The John Innes Horticultural Institute was founded 1910 at Merton, London, SW19, hence the part name of the cherries, but in 1953 it moved to Bayfordbury, Hertfordshire and then to Norwich in 1969.

Merton Glory. Early to mid-season; white. Raised by the John Innes

Horticultural Institute by crossing Ursula Rivers with Noble. 1947.

Napoleon Bigarreau (known to pickers as Naps). White. Origin uncertain but first recorded as Lauermann Bigarreau in Germany, and introduced into England in 1832 and called Napoleon much later. It is thought unlikely that the variety grown today is the original Napoleon that may possibly have had its name changed to Wellington around the time of Waterloo because of the unpopularity of the French in England.

Ohio Beauty (known to pickers by first part of name only, Ohios). White, raised by Professor Kirtland of Cleveland, USA; introduced into England in 1847.

Turk. Black. A cherry grown to use for dye. Branches tend to snap like a carrot and without warning,

Waterloo. Black. Raised by Thomas Andrew Knight, from Ambree crossed with May Duke. Fruited at Elton Hall for the first time shortly before the battle, hence its name, and introduced into Kent in 1815.

A Morello cherry tree.

Culinary purpose cherries

The smaller culinary purpose cherry varieties are able to set their fruit with their own pollen. Some varieties will also pollinate other culinary varieties. The sour or acid flavoured, firm-fleshed fruit is chiefly used for home-made jams and syrups but has also various other commercial uses.

The colour of the various varieties ranges from pale to dark red almost black, the juice being colourless or coloured according to the cherry variety, the stone yellow, rounded-oval. Varieties are:

Flemish or Flemish Red. A small, heart-shaped slightly acid cherry with pale red skin and flesh, self-pollinating; ripe late July; classified as an Amorelle cherry, a culinary cherry which has colourless juice, to distinguish it from the smaller Morello type cherries that have coloured juice. It might possibly have been one of the varieties imported by Richard Harris from Flanders in 1533 and classified as a Flemish cherry. In the late sixteenth century the Earl of Leicester had a thirty acre orchard of this cherry at Sittingbourne which, claimed Samuel Hartlib, 'produced cherries in one season that sold for £1,000'.

Kentish Red. Similar to Flemish Red; a scarlet cherry, but has larger fruit that ripens earlier in July. Pollinated by the Morello or will set a crop with its own pollen. It was being grown in mid eighteenth century Kent and possibly earlier.

May Duke, early name, The Duke. Halfway between the sweet cherries and the Morello cherry, a hybrid of the sweet *Prunus avium* and the acid *Prunus cerasus*; self pollinating. One of the first cherries bred in Kent and not imported, although there is an unsubstantiated belief it was introduced from France about 150 years ago, the name being a corruption of Medoc, the province where it supposedly originated.

Morello. Low, densely branched, bushy tree, sometimes wider than high; self pollinating. Known to John Gerard, author of the *Herball,* in 1597 but became more popular in Kent in the eighteenth century when it was grown as a small tree in garden beds or trained as espaliers against walls. It was sometimes known as the Morella or Milan Cherry, and it was grown to conserve the fruit or eat raw with sugar. The juicy, acid fruit, when dark red, is ready for cooking, stewing, bottling and for making into jams and syrups. When purple-black and sharply sour flavoured it is used by country folk to make a cherry brandy. Sometimes the fruit was difficult to pick by hand, as it was not easy to part the strig bearing the cherry from the twig, so gathering was done with scissors.

A famous Kent product was Thomas Grant's Morella Cherry Brandy, first made in Dover in the 1840s and then in Maidstone until 1960 when E Leslie Grant died and the company ceased as a family business. Thomas Grant obtained his Morello cherries from the area around Ashford and Maidstone, from the valley between the North Downs and what is called the stone hills ridge where the soil was ideal for growing the crop. In the 1890s he also owned 20,000 Morello trees in his orchards at Lenham. Other Morello growers, at Charing Heath and Lenham Heath, also supplied to him,

Some of the other cherry varieties grown in Kent include: **Adams Crown,** white; **Victoria Black**; **Noble,** white; **Webbs Black**; **Emperor Francis** (Emperors), black; **Nutberry,** black; **Goodnestone Black; Noir de Guben,** bred by a Herr Groth of Guben, Germany, black; **Roundel Heart,** heart-shaped, black; **Turkey Heart,** black; **Kent Bigarreau,** white; **Merton Heart,** black; **White Heart,** eighteenth century origin; **Gascoine,** of sixteenth century origin, later **Gascoignes Heart,** from a family involved in cherry growing in the county for several generations; **Black Heart,** of seventeenth century origin; **Black Tartarian,** introduced from Russia, 1796; **Merchant,** from the John Innes Horticultural Institute; **Stella,** a self-fertile sweet variety, bred at Summerland, British Columbia, a cross between an American variety, **Lambert,** and a John Innes bred self-fertile selection; **Van,** self-fertile variety, another Canadian introduction, bred at Summerland as a seedling of the variety **Empress Eugenie.**

At the time of writing the bulk of surviving and newly planted cherry orchards are distributed in the area between Faversham and the Medway Towns. Most of the growers are not planting early or mid-season varieties but are concentrating on the later season black cherry – the varieties favoured by both the multiple retailers and the public.

The current favourites are **Colney, Hertford, Lapins, Stella, Summit** and **Sunburst.** The quantity of acid cherries being grown for culinary use is minute and is usually confined to those farms that have direct sales through pick your own or a farm shop.

9

CHERRIES IN WARTIME

IN the Second World War it was inevitable during the frequent air raids that damage was caused to orchards in the fruit growing districts. Allied and German aircraft crashed among the trees. Enemy bombers jettisoned their bombs into the orchards. Later in the war the doodlebugs dived to earth and exploded among the trees.

In the early 1940s, when still a boy, I was picking with my father in an orchard of damson, cherry and plum trees attached to Berengrove House in Rainham which was owned by Colonel Iremonger – the fruit cultivation being partly an amenity for the house and partly as a supplement to income.

One day a Heinkel 111 flew low over Rainham station and the pilot obviously chose the railway line and bridge across Berengrave Lane as a target. I was at home in nearby Tufton Road and standing in the back garden when I saw a single bomb drop from the aircraft. It missed the railway line and bridge but fell in the colonel's orchard, destroying several cherry and plum trees and wrecking one of the greenhouses. Fortunately the picking season had ended several months previously.

The Ministry of Agriculture, in January, 1940, let it be known that it was not thought to be against the war effort to plant fruit trees in private gardens. It explained in its press release that: 'In an endeavour to increase the staple food crops during wartime it has been necessary to concentrate in the open fields on such crops as cereals and potatoes and to discourage the use of fresh land for trees unless they are planted among the food crops.

'This does not mean, however, that the Ministry of Agriculture deprecates the planting of fruit trees generally. . . The majority of gardeners can grow much of their own fruit without any appreciable loss of ground for vegetables. It is hoped private gardeners will still plant their normal supplies of fruit trees and bushes during the war period bearing in mind that crops should be planted between the trees.'

In the orchards of Kent there was little grubbing up of cherry trees in order to create open land to grow more cereals and potatoes. Neglected or grassed unused marginal land or in the bounds of an orchard was brought back into crop cultivation as in former days.

In the main cherry and other fruit growing continued as before. However, what may seem surprising is that the average yield per tree actually increased from 1940, not reduced as may have been expected. This was because trees planted in the 1930s to replace old, declining trees were beginning to bear fruit. Another factor was the weather. Conditions in summer throughout the war were generally ideal for fruit maturing and picking.

Cherries were greatly in demand as they gave a fillip to rationed foods. All cherries that were available were picked, including the formerly less popular, poor selling or small varieties that in peacetime would have been left on the trees.

This ready sale and the prices obtained encouraged the maintenance of the neglected orchards. What could have had a serious effect on the picking of cherries in their short season was the loss of casual labour, due to the call up for military service or for work of national importance.

Farm workers were in a reserved occupation, producing food to keep down the tonnage that had to be imported. They, with any available part time labour, also worked in the orchards in the picking season and so did the Land Army girls. Where there was a shortfall in number or circumstances demanded the quick availability of pickers to harvest a crop then members of the services were drafted in.

This worked well in most instances but there were occasions when things went awry. Sailors from Chatham were detailed to pick the orchard of Jack Clark at Meres-court Farm, Rainham. They were shown the relevant orchard, provided with ladders, kibsy baskets and boxes and baskets for the picked cherries and left to get on with the job. Sometime later the orchard foreman went to see how the sailors were getting on and he found numerous neatly stacked boxes and baskets full of cherries under the trees. When he examined them he discovered that they were without their strigs – they had been plummed from the trees and would very soon go bad. It appeared that no one had thought to show, or ask, the sailors if they knew how cherries should be picked.

10

DWARFING ROOTSTOCKS AND THE CHERRY'S FUTURE?

FOR more than four hundred years cherries were an important and economically viable crop in Kent but this century has seen a dramatic decline in the acreage under cherry cultivation for a number of reasons.

The varieties planted after the Second World War suffered from bacterial canker, drastically cutting yields; costs of production and marketing continued to rise and there was also the increasing competition of early variety imports from Europe to take the early market in UK before the later Kent varieties were ready. This tended to skim off the interest in cherries so that when English varieties came on to the market would-be buyers had already 'had some cherries'.

Another reason was that a better paid local labour force was not so in need of extra income, so some growers had difficulty in obtaining pickers at the vital time of year. Many of the orchards still had large trees but women pickers no longer had the 'head' to pick at such heights.

From the 1950s cherry acreage fell continually. Often, after being grubbed out, the trees were replaced by apple varieties on smaller trees. In 1951 the area of cherry orchards in Kent in hectares was 5,193; in 1962, 4,223; in 1969, 2,457; in 1975, 1,738; in 1982, 933; in 1988, 550; in 1989, 607; and in 1994, 554 – a fall of 4,639 hectares over forty three years.

Some of these figures can be broken down in acres. At the October, 1966, Orchard Fruit Census there were 7,240 acres under cherry cultivation – 7,143 were sweet varieties, 97 acres Morello/other acid varieties. Of these 291 acres were of trees under four years old: 282 sweet varieties, nine Morello/other acid varieties.

October, 1970, Orchard Fruit Census showed there were 5,470 acres – 5,432 were sweet varieties, 38 acres Morello/other acid varieties. Of these 107 acres were of trees under four years old: 105 sweet varieties, two Morello/other acid varieties.

It is unlikely that the former large trees in their blossom and fruit glory in the orchards will ever return, but a revival in growing smaller cherry trees is already taking place.

It was realised that earlier cropping, high quality, disease-resistant cherry varieties, especially if self-pollinating, were needed. Smaller trees were required so they could be planted at higher tree densities in orchards so making them easier to spray, protect from birds and harvest – perhaps from the ground or a low trestle – so keeping down cultivation and management costs.

With this aim in view East Malling Research Station, as it then was, started working to achieve new resistant, dwarfing rootstocks. The outcome, after testing at the National Fruit Trials, has been the Colt rootstock from a cross between *Prunus avium* and *Prunus pseudocerasus* made in 1958 by the eminent fruit breeder, H M Tydeman.

It is termed semi-dwarfing, eventually growing 15–18ft high. It has shown it is easy to propagate, is compatible with all sweet, acid (Morello), also Duke and ornamental cherry varieties tested. It tends to produce trees with wider angled branches and fruiting precocity as it has large numbers of floral buds in its early years.

This earlier and heavier cropping, with easier tree management, is an advantage. Its disadvantage is poor vigour control with some of the cherry varieties and on some soil conditions. Even so, all plantings over the last several years have been on the Colt semi-vigorous rootstock, but interest is growing in various Continental rootstocks that are more dwarfing than Colt. Growers, however, are now able to keep trees on the Colt rootstock down to a manageable size by the use of the plant growth regulator, Cultar.

The search continues for new, improved dwarfing rootstocks which will produce smaller dwarf trees that can be covered with nets to protect them against bird predation and even by tree shelters to protect the flowers from frost and the fruit from rain. In the meantime the Colt rootstocks are being planted commercially.

A similar search for this type of cherry tree has been going on in Europe since the 1970s. New rootstocks have been bred and tested in Germany – at Weihenstephan and Giessen, with their Weiroot and Gisela rootstocks – and in Belgium, at Gembloux, with their Inmil, Damil and

Camil rootstocks. Several of these have also been tested on trials at East Malling, some with mixed, others with encouraging results. It is likely this will lead to introduction of some of these dwarfing rootstocks, with several varieties, into English cherry cultivation.

Time will tell if high density cherry tree orchards, on dwarfing rootstocks, will become a regular sight in Kent in future. Such a cherry cultivation system should not only make it possible to produce more cherries per orchard, but their tree size make them easier and more economic to cultivate, spray, cover and otherwise manage and harvest.

Perhaps for the first time over a considerable period of years, with the advent of new rootstocks, cherry varieties and cultivation methods, the future of cherry growing in Kent is one that can be anticipated with optimism.

ACKNOWLEDGMENTS

THE author tenders his grateful thanks to the following for their generous assistance to him in the preparation and illustration of this book:

Eddie Barton, Herne, for reading the manuscript and for his experienced advice and useful suggestions for its improvement. George Henthorn, Rainham, for allowing me to visit his cherry orchard at London Road, Rainham, to see and photograph cherry tree varieties. Tony Blake, Chestfield, for his skilful reproduction of original photographs used in this book. Sue Samson, Arts and Libraries Officer, Sittingbourne Library, for research on my behalf.

For information and advice I am most grateful to Jean Hodges, Horticulture Research International, East Malling; Robert Avenell, Statistics Division, Ministry of Agriculture, Fisheries and Food, Guildford and Lynne Thom of the MAFF statistics division in York; Andrew Tinsley, Senior Fruit Consultant, ADAS, Wye; Mrs L Holland, MAFF Helpline, London; Mrs Frances Day, Kent County Agricultural Society, Detling; Mrs Gwen Nabbs, show secretary, Cherry and Soft Fruit Show, NFU Marden; A Richards, Kent NFU, Cranbrook; Rev Derek Ingram Hill, Canon Emeritus, Canterbury cathedral; R B Monk, Folkestone and District Water Company; Brian Tayler, Maidstone Library; M E Ward, group librarian, Shepway; T Masters, group librarian, Sittingbourne; David Cousins, Canterbury Public Library; Gladys Dovey, Rainham, Bill Blake, Chestfield, for taped information supplied. Elizabeth Mountain, Rainham; J Kennett, New Eltham; L M Clark, Lenham; A J Edwards, Canterbury; P Fullagar, Rochester; J G Smith, Lee, SE12; Diana Bailey, Tunbridge Wells; H Chambers, Folkestone; Rev L Owen, former vicar of Teynham; and the Brogdale Horticultural Trust, Faversham, which has 220 cherry varieties in its care so they do not become extinct.

Sincere thanks also to Ray Baldock, Five Ashes; Alan Wilcox, Rainham; Tony Blake, Chestfield; Neil Mattingly, Canterbury; Don Clark, Rainham; and the National Farmers Union, South East Region for supplying me with photographs.

PICTURE CREDITS

Except for those which are credited individually all photographs are by the author or from his collection. This includes some photographs of which he has been unable to trace the photographer or copyright holder and therefore some credits may have been inadvertently omitted, for which he apologises.

BIBLIOGRAPHY

A Pilgrimage of British Farming 1910–1912 by A D Hall.
A Report on the Agriculture and Soils of Kent, Surrey and Sussex by A D Hall and E J Russell, Board of Agriculture and Fisheries, 1911
Cultivated Fruits of Britain – their origin and history by F A Roach. Basil Blackwell,1985.
Dictionary of Gardening, Royal Horticul tural Society. Clarendon Press,1956.
Essays in Kentish History from *Archaeologia Cantiana* edited by Margaret Roake and John Whyman. Frank Cass and Company, 1973.
Flora of Kent by F J Hanbury and E S Marshall, 1899.
Journal of the Royal Horticultural Society. October 1941.
Kent, The Garden of England by Paul Burnham and Stuart McRae. Paul Norbury Publications, 1978.
Life in Kent at the Turn of the Century by Michael Winstanley. Dawson, 1978.
Life in Rural England by W Coles Finch. Daniel and Company, 1929.
Maidstone in 1892 (Illustrated) by E P Edwards. Robinson, Son and Pike.
Seventeenth Century Kent by C W Chalklin, Longmans, 1965.
Teynham Manor and Hundred, 798-1935 by Elizabeth Selby. Meresborough Books, 1982.
The Fruit and the Soil – John Innes Institute. Oliver and Boyd, 1948.
The Shell Book of Country Crafts by James Arnold. John Baker, 1968.
Weald of Kent and Sussex by Sheila Kaye-Smith. Robert Hale, 1953.

Reports

The Economics of Fruit Farming. Report 9: *The Cherry Situation* by A R Hunt and R R W Folley. Wye College, University of London, 1964
Members Day Report: *Cherries – Cherry Rootstock Evaluation* by Dr A D Webster. East Malling Research Association, June 1993.

INDEX

64